May this book create increasing laughter, love, communication and joy in your homes. Never underestimate the power of a family who grow together through dinner time conversations.
We are honoured to be part of your 'table talk' with our 111 fun questions.
We send love from our hearts to wherever this little book may travel,

Lou and Lisa

HAPPY CHILD HAPPY HOME BOOKS

Lou Harvey-Zahra and Lisa Lake have asserted their rights
to be identified as the Authors of this Work

First published in May 2020 by Happy Child, Happy Home Books
Second printing October 2022
www.happychildhappyhome.com

National Library of Australia
Cataloging-in-Publication-Data available
ISBN: 978-0-6488289-0-7
Designed by Darren Evans
Printed and bound by The Printing Hub
in Melbourne, Australia on ethically sourced paper

A message from Lou and Lisa

We are delighted that you have opened the pages of 'Happy Families, Table Talk'. You may simply ask the questions one at a time, from 1 to 111. Or you may play a game of randomly opening the book at a surprise page each evening! This book is named 'Table Talk' but you can take it on a picnic or to grandma's place. Please share it with other families, relatives and friends!

We are not alone in highlighting the power of 'table talk', as researchers throughout the world acknowledge the importance of family communication. When families come together they create bonds through sharing stories and experiences. This book has the magical power to transform meal times into a setting to laugh, share, be heard and connect. It is enlightening to learn new things about each family member and their unique likes and preferences.

This may be just a little book, however, it is our hope that it encourages new conversations, outings and activities into the future, and continues to strengthen connections over time.

When we refer to 'family', we are embracing all the different kinds of families that exist in our wonderful world.

Q:1

Can you think of **three things**
that you are **grateful** for?

Q:2
Name your favourite meal,
breakfast, lunch or dinner.
What do you enjoy about it?

Q: **3**

Name your **favourite** item of **clothing**. How does it make you **feel**?

Q:**4**

If you could only take **one** thing to
a **desert island**, what would it be
and how would **you use it**?

Q:**5**

If **you** could have a **new pet,**
what would it be and
what would you **name** it?

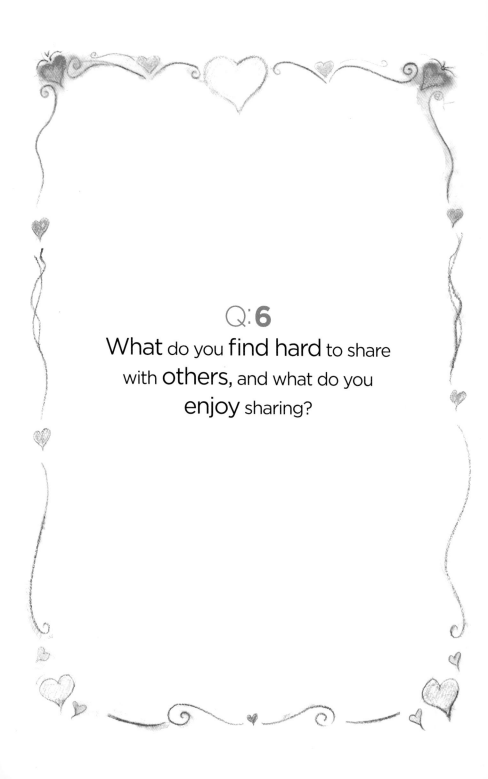

Q: **6**

What do you **find hard** to share
with **others,** and what do you
enjoy sharing?

Q: 7

Can you think of **three things** that make you **unique?**

Q:8

If you could **invite** anyone to
dinner, who would it be and **why?**

Q: **9**

If you were **King** or **Queen** for a day,
what **rule** would you make for
the **people** in your **kingdom?**

Q:**10**

What is your **favourite** smell?
How often do you **smell it?**

Q:**11**

When was the last time
that you felt surprised?

Q:**12**

Explain your day as a **weather** report.
Was it cloudy, sunny, rainy, windy,
with rainbows or **changeable?**

Q:**13**

What is your **favourite** flower?
Who would you like to
give a **bunch of flowers** to?

Q:**14**

Describe your **dream job.**

Would you like to be a wildlife ranger, pilot,
astronaut or **something** else?

Q: **15**

Can you **recall** something
that took a lot of **effort** to do or learn?

Q:16

Would you rather travel on a
ship or a plane, and where
would you go?

Q:17

Can you share three things
that made you happy today?

Q:18

What activities help you to
feel peaceful and calm?

Q: 19

When was the last time
you laughed so hard
that you had to hold your tummy?

Q: **20**

If **you** could have a **zoo animal** as a **pet,** what would you **choose** and why?

Q: **21**

What is your favourite **flavour**
of **ice cream,** and has it
changed over time?

Q: **22**

What is your **favourite** **outside** activity, and why do you **like it?**

Q: **23**

What is, or was, your
favourite **childhood toy?**
What do or did you **enjoy** about it?

Q:**24**

Can you describe the most **amazing**
sight that you have ever **seen?**

Q: 25

What season do you like the best:
Autumn, Winter, Spring or Summer
and why?

Q:26

When was the last time you felt cranky, and what helped you to feel better?

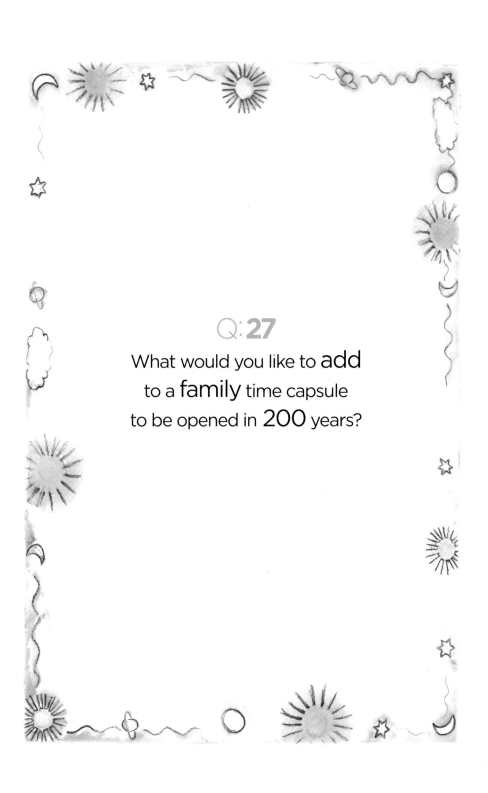

Q: **27**

What would you like to **add**
to a **family** time capsule
to be opened in **200** years?

Q: **28**

What's your favourite flavour of
pizza, and has it changed over time?

Q: **29**

What **magical power** would you like?
Would you rather be **invisible**, be able
to **fly** or to be **super strong**?

Q: **30**

What is your favourite fruit,
and what do you like about it?

Q:31

What would you like to
do more of with your family?

Q: **32**

What is your **favourite**
wild animal, and why do you **like** it?

Q: 33

Which **story book** character
would you like to **meet,**
and **what** would you ask them?

Q: **34**

What do you think your **parent**
or **parents** do at **work?**

Q: **35**

Can you think of a joke or a riddle
and share it with **everyone**?

Q: **36**

Who would you like to say 'thank you' to and why?

Q: **37**

What **instrument** would you like
to **play** in an **orchestra** or **band?**

Q: **38**

What are you looking forward to
doing tomorrow?

Q: **39**

Can you **tell** me the last **time**
that you **helped** someone?

Q: **40**

If **you** could be a **butterfly**,
what **colour** would your **spots** be?

Q: **41**

If a **genie** gave you **three** wishes,
what would they be?

Q: **42**

Name a **song** that you like to sing and **sing it!**

Q: **43**

Can you remember a time
when you needed to use courage?

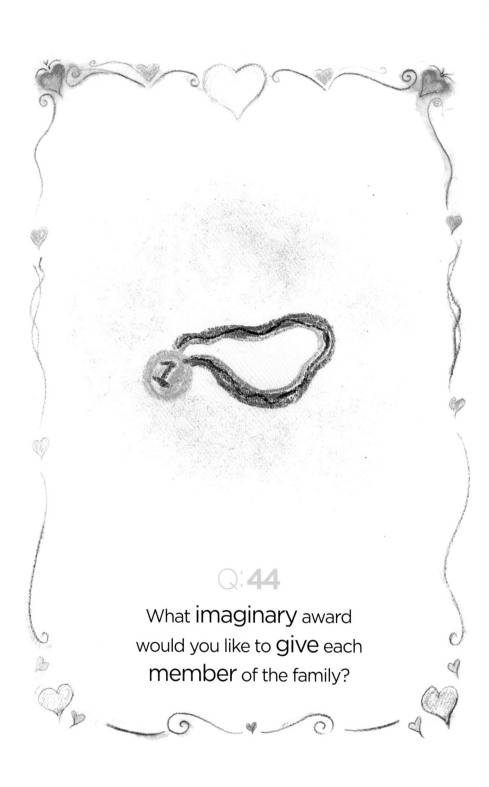

Q:44

What imaginary award
would you like to give each
member of the family?

Q: **45**

Would you rather **ride**
a horse or a motorbike **every day?**

Q: **46**

Using the **first letter** of their **name**,

can you say something **nice** to

each **person** at the table?

Q: **47**

Can you **describe** something **funny**
that **happened** this week?

Q: **48**

Are you a **cat** or **dog** person,
or do you **like** both?

Q: **49**

If you had an **extra hour** of your day,
what would **you do?**

Q: 50

If your **pet** could talk,
what is one thing it would **tell you?**
If you **don't** have a pet what about
your **soft toy?**

Q: **51**

What is the **funniest** sound you can **make?**

Q: **52**

Can you **remember** your favourite
family holiday?

Q: 53

What is your **favourite** tree?
Describe its height, colour,
leaves, fruit or flowers?

Q:54

If you were asked to give every family member at the table a new name, what would you choose?

Q: 55

What makes you feel better
when you are sad?

Q: **56**

Would you like to **fly** like a
bird or swim like a dolphin **and why?**

Q:**57**

What is your favourite **colour,**
and how does it **make** you feel?

Q: **58**

If you had a **special** day with
each **person** in your family,
what would you do **together**?

Q: **59**

What do you **look forward** to
when you **wake up** in the morning?

Q: **60**

If you could **choose,** would you prefer to **play** in the **snow** or at the **beach?**

Q: 61

Would you like to live in
the city or the country and why?

Q: **62**

What would you like to invent?

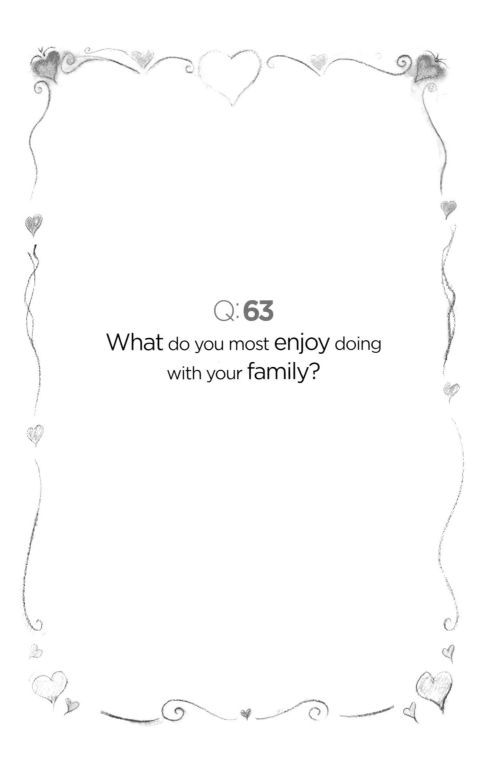

Q:**63**

What do you most **enjoy** doing
with your **family?**

Q: **64**

If you **went** on a **magical bus** adventure
where would **you go?**

Q: **65**

Would you like to be
a **unicorn** or a **dragon,** and
what would **you** do during the day?

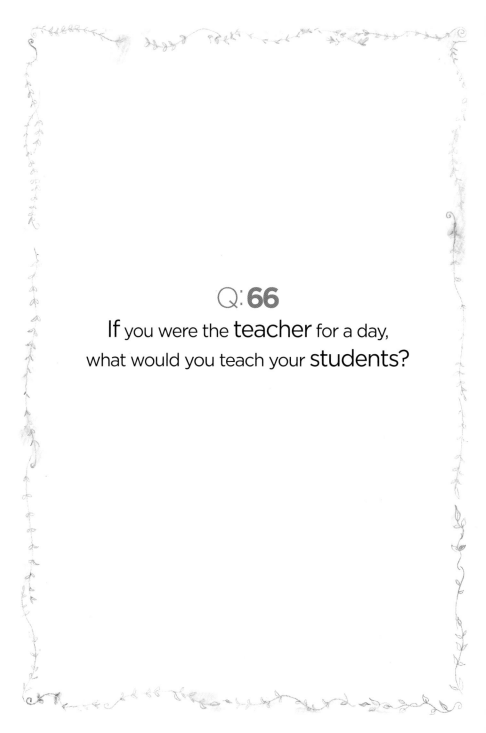

Q: **66**

If you were the **teacher** for a day,
what would you teach your **students**?

Q: **67**

What is your **favourite** sense:

sight, sound, smell, touch or taste?

Q: **68**

If you created a **new planet,**
what would it **be like?**

If you **wrote** a book, what would it
be **about,** and what would the **title be?**

Q: **70**

What is your **favourite day**
of the **week** and why?

Q:71

Which meal could you eat
every day for a week?

Q: **72**

Do you **prefer** to draw, read or
make things, and why do you **enjoy it?**

Q: **73**

Do you have a **party trick?**
If so **show** us.

Q:**74**

What do **you** like to do
at **school** or **work**?

Q: **75**

What is **something** you
would like to **learn** how to do?

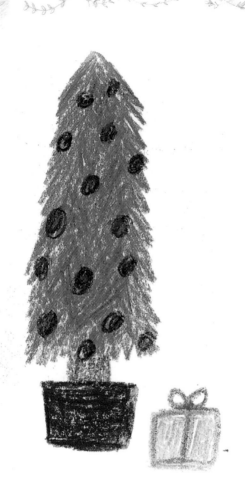

Q:76

If there was a **mystery** present under
the Christmas tree, who would it **be for**
and what would **be in it?**

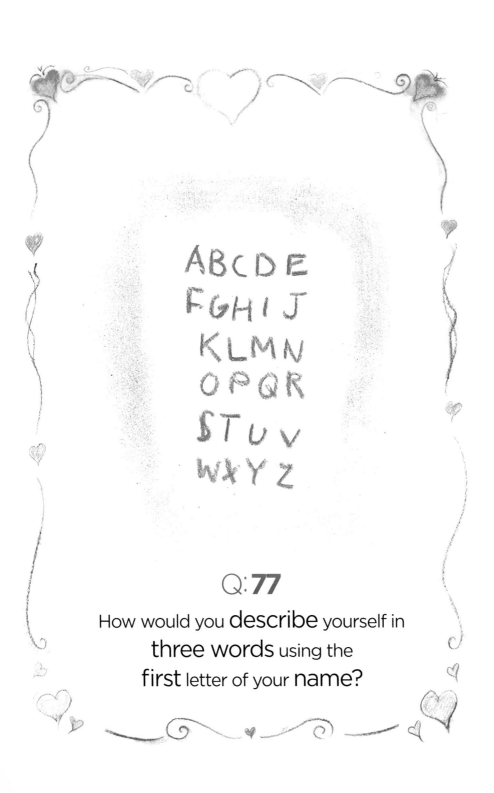

ABCDE
FGHIJ
KLMN
OPQR
STUV
WXYZ

Q:**77**

How would you **describe** yourself in
three words using the
first letter of your **name?**

Q: **78**

Can you **tell** me **something** you enjoyed **today?**

Q:**79**

If you could ask a **wild animal** a **question** what would it be?

Q: **80**

What do you like to do on
a rainy day?

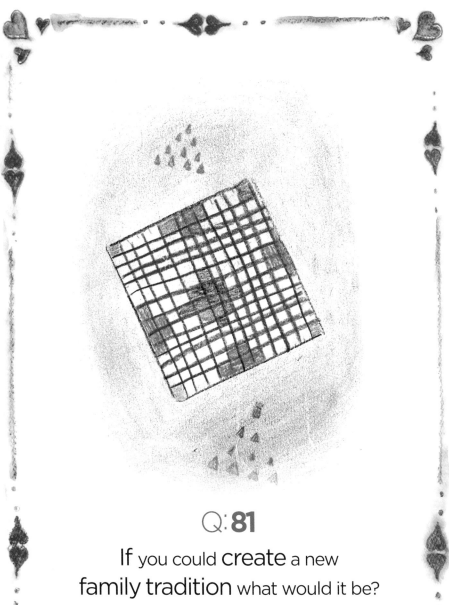

Q: **81**

If you could **create** a new
family tradition what would it be?

For example, Pancake Sunday,

Board Game Friday or something else.

Q: **82**

What is your **favourite** thing about a **birthday party?** Tell us about the **best** party that you have ever **attended.**

Q:83

What is something that
I don't already know about you?

Q: **84**

Describe **three things** that you like in your **bedroom** and **why?**

Q: **85**

Can you tell **everyone** something
wonderful about the person
sitting on your right?

Q:**86**

What could you do to **make**
the world a **better** place?
Pick up rubbish, plant a tree,
reuse jars and pots, recycle paper...

Q:**87**

Can you **describe** a
vegetable or fruit without
naming it?

Q: **88**

Would you rather live in
a castle, teepee or log cabin
and **why?**

Q: 89

If you were a **chef** what restaurant would you **own,** and what would be your **specialty** dish?

Q: **90**

What is your favourite **outside** activity?
Would you like us to do **more** of it
as family **together**?

Q: **91**

What is the most **delicious** meal
that you have ever **eaten** and
what did it **taste like?**

Q:**92**

If you were a **Principal** of a school,
what **new rule** would you **make?**

Past ⟷ Future

Q: **93**

Would you like to **travel** to the
past or the **future** and **why?**

Q: **94**

Using the **letter** of your first name,
can you say **3 things** that you **enjoy?**

Q: **95**

Who in your extended family
would **you** like to spend **more time** with?

Q: **96**

If you could hitch a **ride** in a
rocket ship, where would **you go?**

To the Moon, Saturn, a black hole...

Q: **97**

What is your favourite **board game**,
and do we **play** it enough?

Q: **98**

How could you help someone
this **week**?

Q:**99**

What would you like to grow
in the garden, and what
would you do with it?

Q:100

If you were a **photographer**
what would you photograph?

Do you prefer to **travel** on
a **train** or a **bus?** Tell us about a
journey that you went on.

Q:**102**

If you could be **invisible** for a
short time, what **would** you
like to do?

Q:**103**

What do you **like** most about
your **home?**

Q:104

Can you **describe** your favourite **memory**
of Christmas or another **festival?**

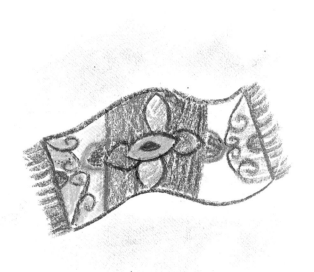

Q:105

If you had a **magic carpet,**
what **natural** world treasures
would you like **to see?**

Q:**106**

What is your **favourite**

vegetable and why?

Q: **107**

What makes you feel **loved?**

Q:108

Adults: What do you think is the **best** thing about being a **child**?

Children: What do you think is the **best** thing about being a **grown up**?

Q:109

What is your favourite cake,
and when would you like to
bake it for everyone?

Q: 110

Tell me something you like about your sibling (or if you don't have a sibling, choose a friend or cousin).

Happy Families,
Table Talk

by
Lou Harvey-Zahra
Lisa Lake

Q: 111

What did you **enjoy** most
about this **book**?

About the Authors and Illustrators

Lou Harvey-Zahra is a popular parenting author with 6 books, teacher and parent of two adult children. When looking back at family life over the years, simple daily conversations and laughter rise to the top of her list of favourite memories. She is excited that families now have this small but special book. For children to listen to parents' stories and also share their thoughts and experiences is so simple, yet so valuable to family well-being. Never underestimate the power of 'table talk' for happy families.

Lisa Lake is a co-author of this book and a mother of two young teens. She is passionate about bringing families together, and strongly believes 'table talk' offers families the opportunity to connect at the end of each busy day. When Lisa met Lou 'table talk' wasn't part of her family rhythm, and she quickly discovered how valuable chatting together was to form strong family bonds. She feels honoured to be able to share what has become so important to her and her family.

Cindy, Danté, Scarlett, Charlie, Poppy and Josie are our wonderful illustrators. They all enjoy 'table talk' and spending time with their families on bike-rides, beach trips, playing board games, visiting the playground and eating ice-cream! Cindy is our cover illustrator, and she enjoys long walks with her family and the dog, reading stories together, and of course drawing.

Also available by Lou Harvey-Zahra

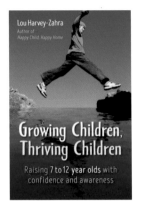

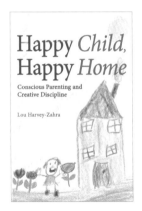
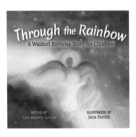

For Lou's books, online parenting courses,
Nurture the Child membership, newsletter and more…

Visit
www.happychildhappyhome.com